MW00603465

The

Compassion Fatigue

Workbook:

28 Exercises for Compassion-Fatigued Helping Professionals

Michelle Graff

Cultivating Human Resiliency

Cultivating Human Resiliency, Kansas City, MO

resiliencyonline.com

© 2021 by Michelle Graff

All rights reserved

Cover Design: Kelsey Klockenteger

ISBN: 978-1-7358817-1-3

Table of Contents

Organizational Culture

Preface

The Compassion Fatigue Workbook: 28 Exercises for Compassion-Fatigued Helping Professionals is intended to be used as a companion guide to the book, *The Compassion Fatigued Organization: Restoring Compassion to Helping Professionals*. Though this workbook could be used by itself, the book provides a more in-depth examination of compassion fatigue. It also provides a context for how these exercises can help individuals and organizations combat compassion fatigue.

This workbook is organized into three sections:

- Self-regulation and Self-awareness
- Building Resiliency and Compassion
- Organizational Culture

I recommend first completing the exercises in order and then revisiting certain worksheets as needed. This workbook could also be used in a group setting with colleagues, completing each worksheet individually and then processing together.

The first section is a collection of worksheets designed to heighten awareness of symptoms, triggers, and responses. The goal is to increase your ability to regulate and restore a sense of safety when triggered.

The second section is a collection of worksheets designed to reinforce the six skill sets for combating compassion fatigue as outlined in *The Compassion Fatigued Organization*:

- Establishing Boundaries
- Exercising Empathy
- Expressing Gratitude
- Processing
- Connecting
- Planning for Self-Care

The goal is to become more resilient and increase your capacity for compassion without feeling depleted.

The third section is a collection of worksheets designed to help assess and improve organizational culture. The goal is to identify organizational symptoms of compassion fatigue, turn symptoms into strengths, and create a culture of compassion.

Many of the exercises in the first two sections can also be used in organizations or group settings. Likewise, the exercises in section three can also be helpful to individuals. Each worksheet is preceded by information to provide context and instructions for how to use the worksheet.

Self-awareness and Self-regulation

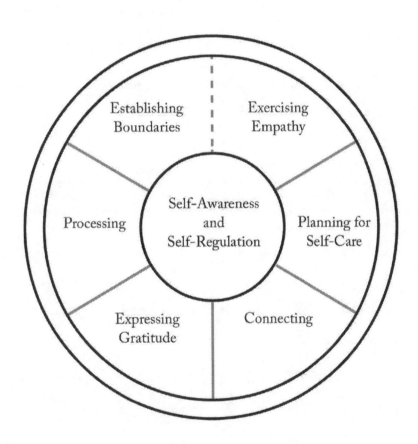

Symptoms of Compassion Fatigue

Not surprisingly, the symptoms of secondary trauma mirror symptoms of primary trauma. In the case of compassion fatigue, the threat becomes the compassionate work we do. When our brains interpret an action as a threat, our body is triggered to fight, flight, or freeze. These responses manifest as physical, emotional, and/or cognitive symptoms. Sufferers of compassion fatigue can experience symptoms of arousal triggered by our fight and flight responses as well as symptoms of avoidance through a freeze response.

Cognitively, arousal responses can include extreme or negative thinking, intrusive thoughts, increased cynicism, disturbing dreams, and rumination. Avoidant cognitive thinking includes minimizing the pain of others, difficulty focusing, impaired decision making, and disassociation.

Emotionally, arousal responses can include irritability, anger, irrational fears, and experiences of emotional overload. Emotional avoidance includes numbing, depression, dread of work, diminished enjoyment, and detachment.

Physical symptoms of arousal include sleeplessness, headaches, and digestive problems, including loss of appetite. Physical freeze responses include diminished energy, immobility, and exhaustion.

Since helping professionals have different experiences and coping resources, their symptoms will also vary. Use the following worksheet to identify your own experience with compassion fatigue. Circle the symptoms that you recognize. This list is not all-inclusive. Identify and write in symptoms that fall into the categories that are not already mentioned.

Symptoms of Compassion Fatigue

Cognitive

Increased cynicism
Repetitive thoughts
Extreme/negative thinking
Intrusive dreams

_____

_____

Difficulty focusing
Impaired decision making
Minimizing others' pain
Dissociation

_____

_____

Emotional

Irritability
Anger
Anxiety
Irrational fears
Despair

_____

_____

Depression
Dread of work
Diminished enjoyment
Numbing
Detachment

_____

_____

Physical

Sleeplessness
Headaches
Digestive problems

_____

_____

Diminished energy
Immobility
Exhaustion

_____

_____

Fight, Flight, and Freeze

The responses of flight, fight, and freeze are built-in protective mechanisms that are triggered automatically when we detect a threat. Awareness of our thoughts, emotions and body responses helps us to understand what and why situations are interpreted by our brains as threatening.

The autonomic nervous system is divided into two parts, the sympathetic and the parasympathetic. The sympathetic response is that of mobility. It is designed to prepare our body for action. This response is often characterized as flight or fight. When activated, pupils dilate, breathing and heart rate increases, and blood circulation is diverted to larger muscles to increase the ability to mobilize to defend. Areas that the brain deems as less necessary are inhibited.

When the parasympathetic system is triggered, the body returns to its normal functioning. The heart rate lowers, with circulation returning to all areas of the body. This allows fine motor functioning and cognitive abilities to be restored. Breathing becomes steadier and less critical functions are restored.

When we are faced with a threat that is too great to fight or flee, a freeze response is triggered. At that point, our bodies become immobilized, and systems begin to slow towards a halt.

Fight, flight, and freeze can also manifest in our emotions. When we are emotionally regulated, both positive and negative emotions have varying nuances and complexity. Yet when triggered into a survival response, our emotions can be reduced to anger (FIGHT), anxiety (FLIGHT), and depression or numbness (FREEZE).

Cognitively, the fight or flight response is distortion and defensiveness. When in survival mode, our brains distort information to facilitate a protective response. The brain's cognitive freeze response is denial or dissociation.

Use the following worksheet to heighten your awareness of your own responses. It is helpful to routinely identify where you fall on the regulation continuum physically, emotionally, and cognitively. We want to be able to recognize when we are regulated and when we are not.

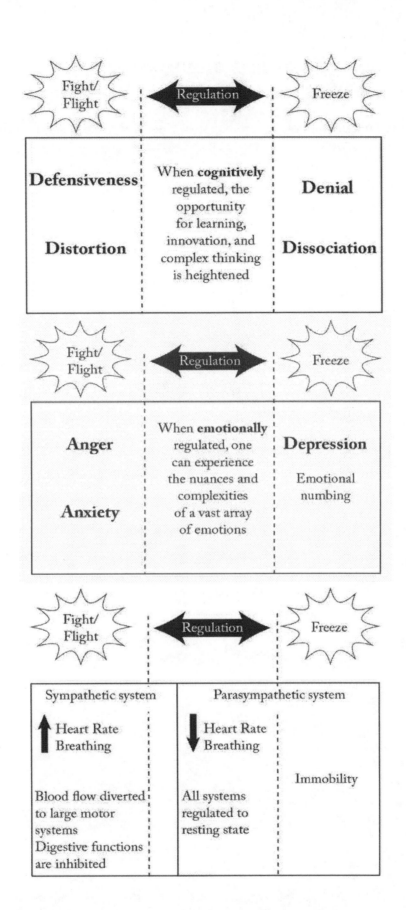

Increasing Response Awareness

The more we become aware of our fight, flight, and freeze reactions, the easier it is to regulate and choose proactive responses.

Self-awareness involves recognizing the ways our survival responses manifest in our body, emotions, and thoughts. It also includes recognizing how our survival responses behaviorally manifest in relationships.

As you continue to learn, use the following worksheet to jot down these insights.

Fight/Flight		Freeze
	Behavioral Responses	
	Cognitive Responses	
	Emotion Responses	
	Body Responses	

Emotional Triggers

Memory is encoded with emotions to help our survival brain identify threats and determine what causes pleasure and what causes pain. But the complex brain is not just built for survival. Humans can experience many more emotional nuances than pleasure and pain. But when in survival mode, the brain generalizes. Therefore, some emotions are interpreted as threats.

To survive in this world, we either need to control external threats or manage them with our external or internal resources. This requires that we either be extremely competent, belong to a community to protect us, or have complete control over our environments. When an emotion signals to the brain that one of these needs are compromised, they become triggers for responses of fight, flight, or freeze.

Self-awareness is not just recognizing when we have been triggered, but also understanding what our emotional triggers are. Triggering emotions can include, but are not limited to:

- Shame
- Envy
- Grief
- Overwhelmed
- Lonely
- Betrayed
- Rejected
- Scared
- Unwanted
- Judged
- Ignored
- Undermined
- Helpless

Use the following worksheet to begin identifying which are your trigger emotions and why.

Emotional Triggers

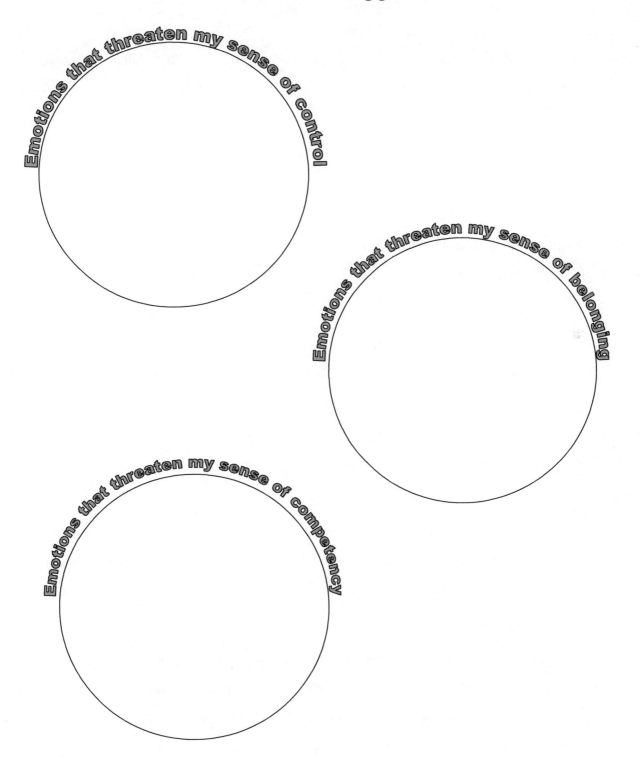

Mind Traps

The brain routinely generalizes and assimilates information to learn and adapt. When in survival mode, the brain uses these functions to stay safe in ways that can alter our perception of the world. When this altered perception interferes with rational thinking, we call it a mind trap.

Polarized Thinking: When the goal is survival, the brain does not need to be distracted with complexity. It simplifies things by narrowing the categories of identification, resulting in a polarized view of reality. This polarized view can help to make quick, lifesaving decisions. But it can also cause us to see only two choices when there is a continuum of possibilities or lead us to perceive something must be one or the other, when both possibilities can exist.

Scarcity Bias: When threatened, the brain performs a mental triage so that all available resources can be used to survive. When the survival brain conducts this inventory of resources, it is only focused on what is available in the here and now. It assumes all resources are finite, even if it is replenishable. When compassion is viewed as a finite resource, we run the risk of perceiving it as something that needs to be conserved.

Time Distortion: Our brain hyper-records sensory information when it detects danger, slowing the perception of time. This can cause us to attribute too much weight to past experiences. What happened in the past can feel as if it is occurring in the present. We also forget the temporariness of the present. When things are unpleasant, it feels like it lasts forever. Time distortions can cloud our ability to make decisions. Overemphasis of the past can also interfere with our ability to envision the future, resulting in a diminished sense of hope.

Negativity bias: The survival brain is hyper alert to danger. It knows the consequence of ignoring a threat is usually greater than the consequence of assuming the worst. This negativity bias can cast a shadow over everyday decisions. It leads us to overgeneralize perceived threats. It also causes us to miss the positive aspects of a situation, limiting our access to possible solutions.

Use the following worksheet to identify how these four mind traps are influencing your decisions, practices, and/or responses in ways that contribute to your compassion fatigue.

Mind Traps

NEGATIVE BIAS

SCARCITY BIAS

POLARIZED THINKING

TIME DISTORTION

Anatomy of a Stuck Mindset

Dr. Bessel van der Kolk, a pioneer in the study of trauma and trauma treatment, describes traumatization as when both our internal and external resources are inadequate to cope with an external threat. There are three parts of traumatization that challenge our basic survival needs:

- External threat (there is something beyond my control)
- External resources (my protective community failed me)
- Internal resources (I was not capable of self-protection)

Over time, if the traumatic exposure continues, a pervasive belief can begin to develop that:

- The world is unsafe
- I am unworthy of belonging
- I am incapable of protecting myself

This worldview paints a reality that offers no protection, something our survival brain does not tolerate well. As a result, a protective mindset can develop that believes:

- I must be in control
- My worth needs to be externally validated, so I can belong
- Someone else needs to be responsible

This stuck mindset can result in unhelpful and even destructive responses. This can lead to unresolved conflicts and strained relationships that further exacerbate compassion fatigue.

Use the following worksheet to begin identifying your own thought patterns and beliefs.

Anatomy of a Stuck Mindset

Trauma	An external threat	which we lack the external resources	and internal resources to cope
Deprivation of safety need	Beyond my control	My protective community failed me	Not capable of self-protection
What situations do your sense of control, belongingness, or capability feel most threatened?			
Pervasive beliefs	The world is uncontrollable and unsafe	My community will not protect me. (Unworthy of belonging)	I am incapable of protecting myself
In what ways do these experiences support a pervasive belief?			
Protective beliefs	I must be in control	My worth needs to be validated so I can belong	Someone else needs to be responsible
In what ways do your responses reflect a protective belief?			

Relationship Responses

Unhealthy relationship responses are often labeled as persecutor, rescuer, and victim responses. Dr. Stephen Karpman first introduced this concept as the "Drama Triangle." It has since been used in the trauma informed movement to illustrate relationship reenactments. Past experiences create patterned responses to relationship stressors. These responses can be as much driven by our past traumas as current situations.

Instead of just labeling, it is important to acknowledge that these are survival responses. Like all triggered survival responses, the three roles of the drama/reenactment triangle (persecutor, rescuer, and victim) represent the fight, flight, and freeze response as they occur in behavioral interactions.

In the role of the persecutor, we have been triggered into a fight response. Common persecutor responses involve threats, name-calling, labeling, vilifying, and other coercive behavior.

In the role of rescuer, we have usually been triggered into a flight response. Rescuer behavior is a veiled attempt to flee an uncomfortable emotion or circumstance. Common rescuer behavior involves fixing other people's problems, so we do not have to watch them struggle. Rescuer behavior can also involve avoiding conflict, both internal and external, by pacifying the situation. These flight responses can also include minimizing another's emotions or withholding information to avoid a negative response.

Finally, in the role of the victim, we have been triggered into a freeze response. Common victim responses involve passively waiting for someone else to solve their problem for them or failing to take responsibility for their own actions.

Think of a recent conflict or conflicts and use the following worksheet to identify your own fight, flight, or freeze relationship responses.

Relationship Responses

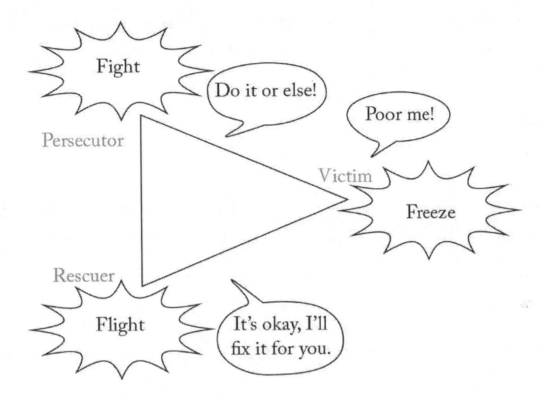

FIGHT	FLIGHT	FREEZE

Shifting Relationship Mindsets

A protective mindset can begin to permeate our beliefs about relationships. Stuck thinking patterns can emerge that keep us locked into triangle response patterns. Such thinking includes:

- **Blaming:** Someone needs to be blamed or punished to control the situation.
- **Entitlement:** I am owed something, and I need external validation of my worth.
- **Helplessness:** I do not have the power to change things for the better

When faced with interpersonal conflict, the thought patterns of the protective mindset heighten the perception of threat and increase the likelihood of responding from any one of the triangle roles.

Since stuck mindsets are rooted in threats to our basic human needs, unstuck mindsets involve beliefs that restore a sense of autonomy, belonging, and competence. Such examples include:

- **Ownership:** I am responsible for my own feelings, thoughts, and behaviors (and no one else's).
- **Humility:** I am human, and all humans have flaws, and all humans have worth.
- **Change:** I am not bound by my past abilities; everyone is capable of growth and change.

When we can identify stuck thinking and unhealthy relationship patterns, we create an opportunity for a different response. However, mindsets can be deeply embedded. Change needs to come from more than simply shifting our thinking. It requires different relationship experiences, responses, and habits.

Using the following worksheet, identify some of your unhelpful thought patterns that you get "stuck" in. Write down the thinking that could help you get "unstuck." Recall a recent interpersonal conflict. What ways would this thinking have changed your responses and possibly the outcome?

Shifting Relationship Mindsets

STUCK MINDSET

Entitlement	
Blaming	
Helplessness	

UNSTUCK MINDSET

Humility	
Ownership	
Change	

Reset

The circuit breaker box in our homes provides a good analogy to help us understand compassion fatigue. When we have too many electrical appliances running at once, a circuit breaker will trip, and the power goes out. This is a safety feature. To someone who does not understand how a house is wired or what a circuit breaker is, it would seem like the house lost power. The truth is the electricity has not been depleted; we just need to unplug a few things and reset the circuit breaker to restore power.

Compassion fatigue is our survival response to chronic stress and exposure to the pain and trauma of others. When our amygdala senses a threat, it sends the signal that a protective response is needed. It "trips the breaker" as part of our brain's built-in safety feature. Like when our home seems to be "out of power," symptoms of compassion fatigue include feeling depleted of compassion. This sensation and other symptoms can be better understood by examining how the brain and body respond to threats.

Our autonomic nervous system controls unconscious body functions, such as breathing, heart rate, circulation, and digestion. When the brain sends the distress signal, the sympathetic side prepares the body for fight or flight by increasing heart rate, concentrating blood flow, and slowing down the body functions it determines to be less essential.

In addition to stimulating the "fight or flight" responses of the sympathetic nervous system, the brain can also trigger a "freeze" survival response. This response can include the numbing of emotions and avoiding empathetic responses that leave us vulnerable to more pain.

Helping professionals can be constantly triggered into this freeze response by repeat exposure to secondary trauma. This can lead them to believe that they are depleted of compassion, as it is often described. In fact, this is not the case. Compassion is renewable. Too often, helping professionals do not take the time or are unaware of the need to reset.

Use the following worksheet to identify when we have been triggered or "our breaker has been tripped" and we need to reset.

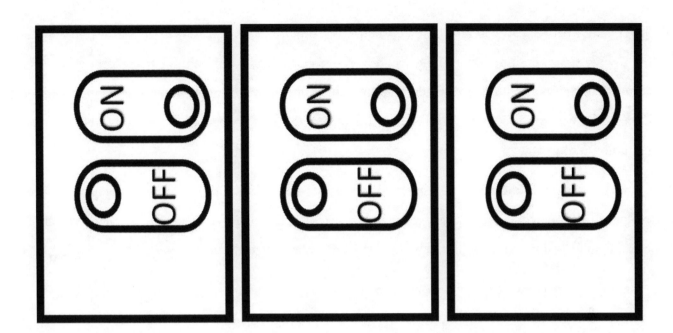

I know I need to reset when...

Regulation Resources

Well-regulated people can ebb and flow between the sympathetic and parasympathetic response systems without being triggered into either flight or fight on one end of the continuum or freeze on the other end. Therefore, self-regulation involves widening our tolerance of emotional triggers and increasing our awareness of our autonomic responses. We do this by employing self-regulation methods, also referred to as regulation resources.

Our neuronal system is bidirectional. Therefore, just as messages of threat trigger a physiological response, physiological actions can trigger messages of safety back to the brain. In fact, the vagal nerve has four times as many pathways connecting the body to the brain than the other direction.

For example, gum chewing produces saliva. Saliva is produced as part of the digestive process in the parasympathetic response. This return to normal functioning signals to the brain and communicates everything is all right. Facial and vocal muscles are also part of the parasympathetic nervous system. Therefore, humming or singing can stimulate a return to a parasympathetic state. These types of regulation resources are what we call *bottom-up*.

Examples of *top-down* regulation resources would include self-talk, visualizing a place of safety or connection, naming feelings, or reaching out to an external resource to process or challenge distorted thinking.

Regulation resources can further be characterized not only as top-down or bottom-up, but as calming or connecting. *Calming* to bring us back from a fight or flight response and *connecting* to engage us from a freeze response of disconnect. Both types of resources bring us back to a state of safety.

The following worksheet is divided into four quadrants (top-down calming, top-down connecting, bottom-up calming, bottom-up connecting.) Use it to identify the regulation methods in each quadrant that you have successfully used in the past. Conducting this activity in a group broadens the available resources as people share their current skill sets. It is also important to identify skill gaps in any of the quadrants.

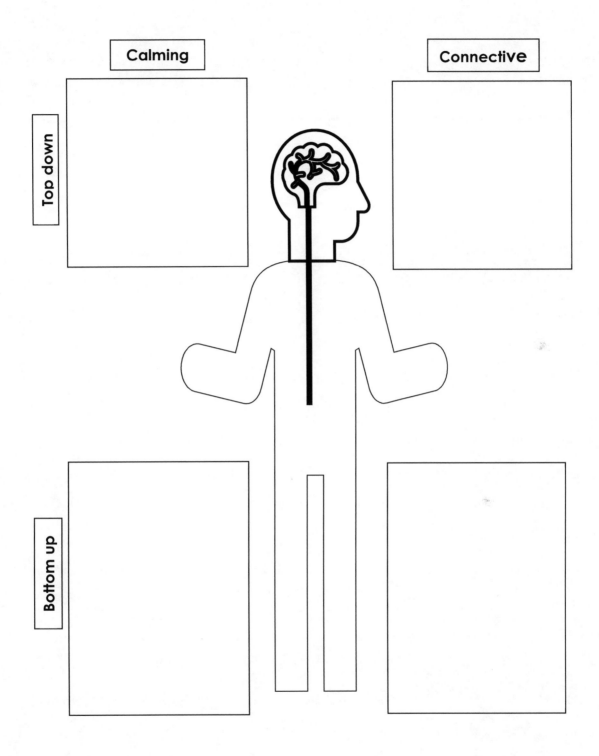

Calming

Connective

Top down

Bottom up

Building Resiliency

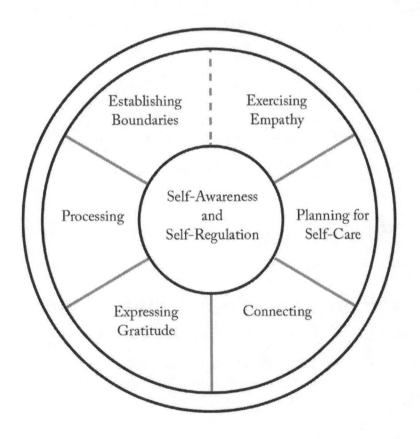

- Establishing Boundaries
- Exercising Empathy
- Processing
- Self-Awareness and Self-Regulation
- Planning for Self-Care
- Expressing Gratitude
- Connecting

Identifying Relationship Needs

To set boundaries, we first determine what is needed in each relationship to be safe and effective. Keep in mind that needs are different for varying relationships. Sometimes it is necessary to start by identifying categories of relationships:

- **Close relationships:** These are people you know well for a long time and are involved in or concerned with most areas of your life. You provide support to each other when needed and there is a commitment to be there for each other in both good and bad times. This can include family members, intimate partners, or long-time friends.

- **Friend relationships:** People who you know well enough to list their qualities and who know you enough to do the same. This is a two-way relationship, but support is optional and not necessarily expected or required. These relationships might be in only one area of your life (family, social, work, church), or sometimes they may cross over into more than one area.

- **Resource relationships:** People with whom we have a necessary relationship because we provide each other with a resource. The relationship might provide either one-way or two-way support. Examples might be your boss, someone who works for you, some coworkers, your doctor, a client, etc.

- **Acquaintances:** People we know, but either do not know well enough to be in any of the other categories or we choose not to put them in any other category.

Recognizing the type of relationship can keep us from blurring the boundaries. It also helps us to better identify the needs of that relationship.

Use the following worksheet to help identify relationship needs. Use a different sheet for each identified relationship or relationship category. Remember that boundaries are bidirectional and so are needs. Therefore, it is important to consider what the other person's needs are as well as your own.

Identifying Relationship Needs

What do you need to accomplish through this relationship?

You:

Other Person:

What do you need to know or learn from each other?

You:

Other Person:

What kind of support do you need from each other?

You:

Other Person:

What is the most important goal of this relationship for each of you?

You:

Other Person:

Identifying Relationship Needs

What do you need to accomplish through this relationship?

You:

Other Person:

What do you need to know or learn from each other?

You:

Other Person:

What kind of support do you need from each other?

You:

Other Person:

What is the most important goal of this relationship for each of you?

You:

Other Person:

Identifying Relationship Needs

What do you need to accomplish through this relationship?

You:

Other Person:

What do you need to know or learn from each other?

You:

Other Person:

What kind of support do you need from each other?

You:

Other Person:

What is the most important goal of this relationship for each of you?

You:

Other Person:

Setting Limits

Limits include what you are willing and not willing to do, give and not give, and reveal and not reveal in your relationships with others. In other words, what we will say yes to and what we will say no to in that relationship.

All people have boundaries that slide along intersecting continuums of loose or tight and clear or unclear. What makes a boundary healthy is not whether its limits are loose or tight, but whether it is clearly communicated, adaptable to varying situations or relationships, and allows us to function safely.

Setting limits involves identifying what you will say yes to and what you will say no to in each boundary area. These limits will vary for each type of relationship and depend on those relationship needs previously identified.

Remember, limits do not have to be set in stone. They can change as relationships change.

Use the following worksheet to begin identifying limits in what you are willing to say yes or no to in your relationships. Think about what you would do or have done, give or receive, and reveal or hear.

Setting Limits

	Yes	No
DO or have done to you **Values** **Responsibility** **Personal Space**		
Give or receive **Time** **Energy** **Resources**		
Reveal or hear **Opinion** **Information** **Emotions**		

Recognizing Cues

Recognizing when your boundaries have been breached involves being attuned to your emotions and body responses to having your boundaries crossed. But it also requires the insight to interpret another's frustrating behavior as a messy attempt to set a boundary.

Most of us have experienced our boundaries being crossed in one way or the other. Remember that boundaries are not just physical. We need boundaries for what we reveal (information, emotions, opinions), what we give (resources, time, energy), and what we do (responsibilities, values, and personal space).

We need to recognize that boundaries are a two-way street. Even someone with clear boundaries can accidentally cross someone else's. But, since people with unhealthy boundaries tend to respond in messy ways, sometimes we do not even recognize their response as a boundary at all. Instead, it is interpreted as hostility, indifference, or rejection. Having healthy boundaries means respecting the boundaries of others, even if they struggle to communicate them.

Learning to recognize the emotional and physical cues for when our boundaries are crossed is a skill set that may need to be developed or fine-tuned. Use the following worksheet to recount times when either your boundaries have been crossed or you have crossed someone else's boundaries in each of the boundary areas. Jot down some of the cues, which can be behavioral, cognitive, emotional, or physical.

Opinions	Emotional	Informational
Personal Space	Energy	Time
Resources	Values and Beliefs	Roles

Clarifying Statement

We clarify our boundaries directly and indirectly through our words and actions. Sometimes, when boundaries are crossed or about to be crossed, it is necessary to make a clarifying statement. A clarifying statement involves identifying the breach and communicating your need(s) It is also helpful to offer what would be acceptable. Here are some examples:

Time Boundary:

- This is becoming more than I can offer. I need to reserve my time on weekends for my family. I could help an hour a month during the week.
- That would mean working through dinner. I set aside dinnertime to be with my family. I am willing to come in early tomorrow to catch up instead.

Responsibility Boundary:

- That is not my responsibility. I want to see you accomplish that on your own. I would be happy to walk you through how it is done.

Emotional Boundary:

- You have shared a lot of strong feelings today. I am confident you will be able to work through this.
- We seem to only talk about negative things. I need to be able to share positive emotions too. Let's make sure we set aside time to talk about possible solutions.

Use the following worksheet to practice developing clarifying statements for boundaries that are commonly crossed in each boundary category. Boundary statements should be kept short. You are not required to overly explain why you have a boundary.

	Clarifying Statement
Values Responsibilities Personal Space	
Time Energy Resources	
Opinions Information Emotions	

Shifting Roles and Responses

Whether responding from the role of persecutor (fight), rescuer (flight), or victim (freeze), we often choose protective devices that perpetuate conflict, trauma, and a stuck world view. These protective devices include coercion, manipulation, and denial. The use of coercion, manipulation, and denial crosses boundaries and damages relationships.

In contrast, responses that offer choice and transparency avoid boundary breaches. These responses promote the restoration of autonomy, belonging, and competency. Thus, the response roles in the trauma triangle shift from persecutor to **coach**, rescuer to **ally**, and victim to **thriver**.

For example, instead of a rescuer response (unsolicited reframe) "You should be thankful, at least you still have a job," an ally response might be, "I can understand your disappointment, when you are ready, I would be happy to help you identify some of the good things you still have to look forward to."

Instead of a persecutor response, "If you don't get with the program, there will be disciplinary action," a coaching response might be, "These are the requirements of this job, if you choose to continue working in this program, let's discuss what that will need to look like and how I can help you be successful."

Instead of a victim response of "It's not fair, this always happens to me," a thriver response might be "What do I need to learn, so this does not happen again."

Think of a time when you responded with coercion, manipulation, or denial. Use the following worksheet to record your responses to the following:

- In what ways was this a boundary violation?
- What response would have demonstrated choice and transparency?

Shifting Roles and Responses

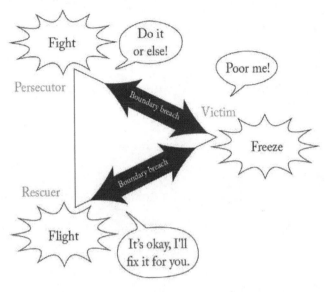

_____

_____

_____

_____

_____

_____

_____

_____

_____

_____

Shifting from Judgment to Understanding

Practicing empathy is an essential part of cultivating compassion. Empathy is the ability to experience another's thoughts and feelings as separate from our own. For the individual, empathy is a complex skill set that involves functions of the prefrontal cortex, autonomic responses, and, of course, our limbic system, which is responsible for much of our emotional processing. The ability to be empathetic evolves according to our developmental experiences and can be strengthened with practice. Exercising empathy involves four components. They include:

- Being present
- Suspending judgment
- Perspective taking
- Emotional attunement.

Being present involves listening with focus. This can be challenging when we are distracted by our own thoughts of judgment.

In situations where you struggle to stay out of judgment, try momentarily letting go of the need for an explanation. Instead, it is more helpful to remind ourselves of the universal things that make us human. In these ways, this person is no different than you or anyone else.

As we move into perception taking, keep in mind that even deliberate attempts to take on another's perspective are filtered through our own lens of understanding. Therefore, like suspending judgment, perspective taking is a skill that requires practice to develop.

Remember that empathy is more than just perspective taking. It also involves emotional attunement. However, deliberate attempts to suspend judgment and take on another's perspective can help us to be more attuned to their emotional experience.

Choose someone whose perspective you are struggling to understand. Use the following worksheet to practice shifting from judgment to understanding.

Shifting from Judgment to Understanding

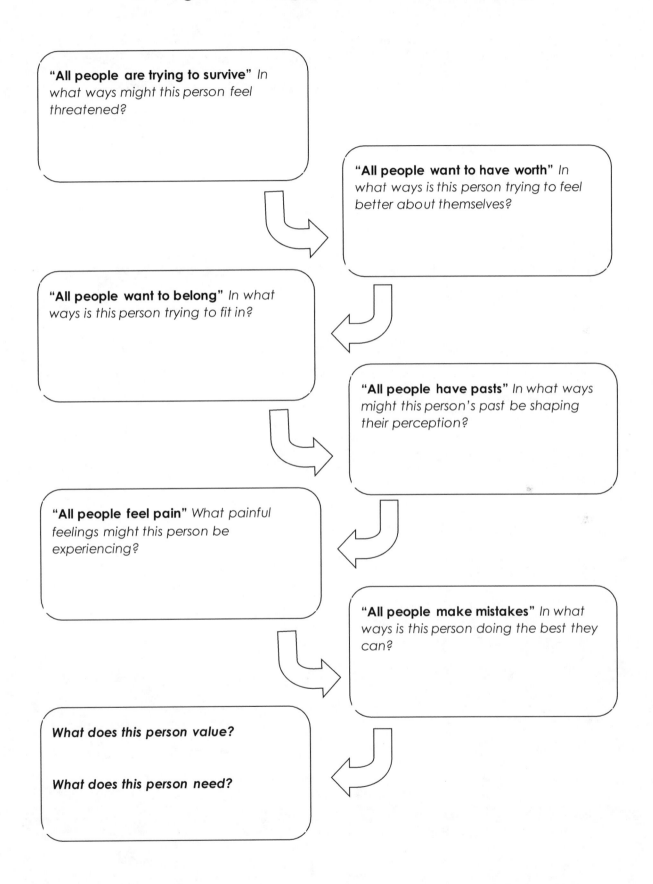

"All people are trying to survive" *In what ways might this person feel threatened?*

"All people want to have worth" *In what ways is this person trying to feel better about themselves?*

"All people want to belong" *In what ways is this person trying to fit in?*

"All people have pasts" *In what ways might this person's past be shaping their perception?*

"All people feel pain" *What painful feelings might this person be experiencing?*

"All people make mistakes" *In what ways is this person doing the best they can?*

What does this person value?

What does this person need?

Practicing Gratitude

Studies have shown a link between gratitude and well-being. It is also a great coping skill for dealing with stress, anger, or depression. The practice of gratitude helps shift our perspective from scarcity to abundance.

Gratitude is a resiliency that can be developed. Like most resiliencies, it involves changing our thinking and cultivating a habit through practice. Here are a few things to try:

- Develop a gratitude routine. Set aside a moment each day to list at least three things for which you are thankful. Better yet, write them down or share them with others.

- Express gratitude in our relationships. Simple expressions of appreciation can be verbal or written. Sometimes it just takes practice.

- Try gratitude in the face of adversity. When life hands us a problem to be solved, we often start by thinking about the difficulties of the situation. Instead, begin by thinking of the resources that will help you find a solution. Whether it is another person or your own resiliency resources, for that, you can be thankful.

Use the following worksheet to begin shifting your thinking from scarcity to gratitude.

Practicing Gratitude

4 things for which I am grateful today

1. _____

2. _____

3. _____

4. _____

4 experiences for which I am grateful

1. _____

2. _____

3. _____

4. _____

4 skills I have for which I am grateful

1. _____

2. _____

3. _____

4. _____

4 people in my life for which I am grateful

1. _____

2. _____

3. _____

4. _____

Routine Processing

A simple practice that individuals can implement is routine processing. Routine processing is a method of acknowledging experiences that offers emotional and concrete support and allows us to let go of our work and be present for our home life.

Individuals can develop processing routines that are a part of their daily rituals. This includes written exercises or list making at the end of the day. Writing things down is a symbolic way of releasing our thoughts. Having them on paper also gives us permission not to keep reviewing what needs to be done while we are away from work. Mental exercises can also be helpful if they include asking a set of questions to process thoughts, feelings, and events. Deep breathing can be used to symbolize the release of feelings and concerns we wish to leave at work.

Co-workers can also offer one-on-one processing. A routine practice at the end of the day can take no more than five to ten minutes.

The following worksheet can be used to develop a daily processing routine.

Routine Processing

- What was the most challenging point of your day?
  (What happened? What emotion did you experience? How did you respond?)

- What was your high point today? (Reflect the emotion)

- What would you like to achieve tomorrow?

- Who can support you in this goal?

Connective Responses

There is a connection between the mindset and response. Shifting mindsets should facilitate a different response. Beliefs, such as ownership, humility, and change, can facilitate connection. It is important that these beliefs are not thought of as a response toward another. Attempting to make another accountable, humble, or change is not likely to facilitate connection. Instead, the mindset of ownership, humility, and change should free us to employ a connective response such as validation, forgiveness, and humility.

- When our mindset is that of humility, we can respond with validation.
- When our mindset is that of ownership, we can respond with forgiveness.
- When our mindset is that of change, we can respond with hope.

Validation: Affirming another's human worth and dignity. This includes validating emotions and experiences. It also includes behaviors that convey respect.

Forgiveness: Letting go of past harms. Although this does not mean letting someone continue to violate a boundary, it does include letting go of a need to seek revenge or see them punished (including emotionally) for past mistakes or misdeeds.

Hope: Instilling in others the belief that growth is possible. This includes focusing on strengths, recognizing small changes, and celebrating successes. It also includes using language that puts problems in the past and acknowledges future skills and resources that can be acquired. For example, using the word "yet" to convey that they will be able to one day overcome their current challenges.

Think of a relationship in which you would like an improved connection. Use the following worksheet to explore both the mindset and examples of connective responses that might help you achieve this goal.

Connective Responses

THRIVER MINDSET

Humility	
Ownership	
Change	

CONNECTIVE RESPONSES

Validation	
Forgiveness	
Hope	

Is It Numbing or Self-Care?

Taking care of oneself is an essential element in combating compassion fatigue and cultivating compassion. Those who suffer from chronic exposure to stress and secondary trauma are left exhausted and can feel a need to shut out the source of their pain. Unfortunately, this leads some to choose activities in the name of "self-care" that involve numbing our emotional connections. This can create a disconnect when what we need is to reconnect.

There is a valid need to transition from work to home. We all occasionally need to unwind from a challenging day's work, especially those who work in stressful environments. However, this should involve identifying feelings, not numbing them.

Numbing can include "vegging" in front of the television, boredom eating, substance use, playing repetitive games on your phone, or mindlessly scrolling through social media. None of these activities are necessarily harmful in themselves. They just might lack the nourishing connection that real self-care can provide. Even worse, it is difficult to selectively numb negative emotions without losing the positive ones. Thus, we are inadvertently denying ourselves the source of genuine healing and revitalization.

Keep in mind, it is not the activity itself that is the problem; it is how you are engaging in it. It is up to you to determine if you are engaging in an activity to numb or to connect.

Use the following worksheet to determine if the activities you are presently engaging in are numbing or connective.

Is It Numbing or Self-Care?

List five activities you have participated in last month:

_____

_____

_____

_____

_____

Ask yourself the following questions for each activity:

- Does this activity help me to feel rejuvenated?

- Does this activity help me to focus?

- Does this activity increase my awareness?

- Can I keep track of time during this activity, as opposed to time slipping away without my knowledge?

- Does this activity help me to sleep better?

When choosing to unwind, pick activities that you can answer yes to the above questions.

Rediscovering Joy

Joy is one of the most connective emotions we can experience. When we are experiencing joy, we are fully engaged and present. So often, our demanding lives and even our own survival responses can prevent us from experiencing true moments of joy.

In my self-care workshops, I like to lead participants in an exercise that involves naming the activities that they did as a child or young adult that brought them joy. So often we push play or other amusements out of our lives because we view them as unimportant or juvenile. When in fact, they can be a valuable contribution to our overall well-being.

Exploring new areas of interest can lead to new opportunities for learning and enjoyment. Recreation and leisure activities can be engaged in solitude or with others, at home or in our community. It is about discovering ways to provide enrichment in your life outside of work.

Use the following worksheet to explore opportunities for joy that you can begin incorporating or reincorporating into your life.

Rediscovering Joy

List three people, places and things that bring you joy?

What activities do you enjoy doing?

When were you the happiest?
What did you do then?

What were your favorite activities as a child?

What hobbies have you enjoyed in the past?

What would you do if you had a day to yourself?

What new things would you like to try or learn?

Connective Self-Care Plan

Effective self-care involves developing habits that incorporate self-care strategies into our regular routines. It is not a reactionary measure to be taken when we are at the end of our rope. Instead, it is a practice that is woven into our daily, weekly, and monthly routines.

The Connective self-care plan is a tool that can help us commit to the practice of regular self-care strategies that are rejuvenating and restorative until they become habits. Use the following worksheet to help generate new ideas. Circle the ideas that seem the most appealing to you or let these ideas spark new ones.

Next, list the actions that you want to commit to doing regularly. Writing things down helps increase the likelihood of follow-through. This is especially true if a desired action has not yet become a habit.

Reevaluate your plan on a quarterly or yearly basis. Once something becomes a habit or is ingrained in our routine, it does not need to be on the plan. If something is no longer helpful or possible, this too can be removed from the plan. Adjust and try new things that fit well into your life circumstances.

Practicing self-care that is connective, instead of numbing, can increase our ability to connect with others, and social connectivity is one of our most powerful sources of healing and resiliency.

Connective Self-Care Plan

Ideas to...

Engage Your Creativity

Write sing craft rap cook
paint build sew dance act
garden rhyme draw play
perform sculpt bake

Engage Your Senses

go to an art gallery go barefoot
spend time in nature aromatherapy
listen to music massage your hands
smell the roses savor good food
pet a pet see a performance

Nourish Your Body

Keep bedtime routines walk bike
practice deep breathing hike
drink water yoga eat clean
meditate exercise play sports
snack nutritiously

Engage Your Mind

read Learn a new skill pray
take a class play puzzles
take up a hobby journal
listen to new ideas

Engage Others

Call a friend movie night volunteer
share your hobby greet neighbors
coffee date host game night
join a book club
visit the elderly
church

I will commit to care for myself routinely by...

Daily

Weekly

Monthly

Organizational
Culture

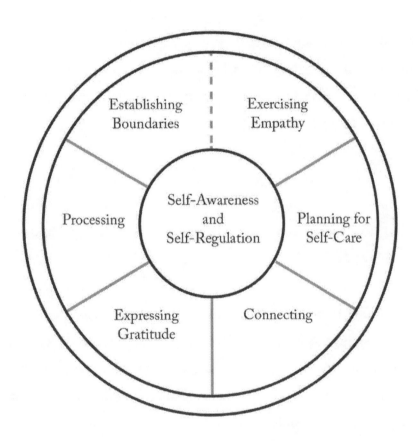

Organization Compassion Fatigue Assessment (short)
Moving from Symptoms to Strengths

Just like individuals, organizations that repeatedly experience secondary trauma and chronic stress develop responses of flight, fight, and freeze. Over time, these can become organizational symptoms of compassion fatigue. Recognition of these symptoms is a core step in creating a compassionate culture.

The following organizational self-assessment tool includes a list of cognitive, emotional, and behavioral responses as they manifest in organizations. Since symptoms can vary in intensity, frequency, and duration, a 5-point Likert scale is used to represent a continuum from symptoms (on the left) to strengths (on the right.) Circle whichever number best represents where you see your organization on this continuum. The *italicized* questions below the scale are meant for guidance to help define the symptoms and strengths as they might manifest in an organization. *Note: This assessment tool is meant for planning purposes and not intended to be scored.*

This tool could either be used as a survey to gather information, or it could be used to record perspectives from different focus groups. The information gathered can then be used to develop goals by identifying symptoms and prioritizing the ones that have the most negative impact on the organization. The goal is to turn symptoms into strengths.

Remember, just as we ask the trauma-informed question "what happened to them," when referring to individuals we serve, we must ask the same question when assessing the organization. The irony of all this is that organizations designed to facilitate a compassionate response to social problems begin to feel like places that hold no space for compassion to thrive. But this is not an accurate reflection of an organization's heart. It is merely a symptom of the same compassion fatigue experienced by the people it employs. The solution, therefore, lies in cultivating a culture of compassion.

Organization Compassion Fatigue Assessment

Scarcity Thinking   1   2   3   4   5   **Abundant Thinking**
Is there a constant pressure to find ways to cut corners and make do with less? Or does the organization prioritize so that programs and staff have the resources they need to be successful?

Blaming   1   2   3   4   5   **Accountability**
Is there a scramble to assign blame? Or do members take responsibility for problems and solutions?

Failure to learn   1   2   3   4   5   **Healthy Innovation**
Does the organization repeat mistakes and expect employees to blindly follow rigid procedures? Or do they embrace both successes and failures as learning opportunities and encourage experimentation?

Fixed Potential   1   2   3   4   5   **Growth Potential**
Are some seen as having fixed roles and capabilities? Or does the organization develop and inspire employees at all levels?

Denial   1   2   3   4   5   **Awareness**
Are leaders unaware of the struggles of their employees, the needs of the community, and potential threats to the organization? Or do they have an accurate perception of challenges?

Polarization   1   2   3   4   5   **Shared Ownership**
Is there a strong us against them mentality between management and frontline, different departments, and even staff and clients? Or do all members have a sense of ownership and collaboration?

Fear   1   2   3   4   5   **Sense of safety**
Is fear the primary motivator? Or do employees feel safe in the knowledge that they will be treated fairly?

Numbing   1   2   3   4   5   **Attunement**
Is there a failure to validate emotions so that negative emotions surface in the form of low morale, absenteeism, and high turnover? Or are there healthy avenues for emotional expression and attunement?

Unresolved Conflict   1   2   3   4   5   **Conflict Resolution**
Do conflicts go unresolved, allowing anger to fester? Or are they addressed in a timely manner?

Reactionary Responses   1   2   3   4   5   **Discernment**
Does the organization react to situations based on past negative perceptions and emotions? Or do they make value-based decisions guided by future expectations?

Punitive Practices   1   2   3   4   5   **Empowerment**
Does the organization try to control behavior through punitive methods? Or does it encourage accountability through clear expectations, learning opportunities and choice?

Closed Communication   1   2   3   4   5   **Transparency**
Is needed information kept hidden? Or is the flow of information bidirectional, clear, and open?

Disconnected   1   2   3   4   5   **Purpose Driven**
Do actions routinely contradict professed values? Or is there a clear connection between the work being done and the mission of the organization?

Organizational Self-Assessment (Long)
Moving from Symptoms to Strengths

This long version of the organizational compassion fatigue assessment is designed to organize the information gathered for use in a plan for change.

The below checklist offers cognitive, emotional, and behavioral responses as they manifest in organizations. Since symptoms can vary in intensity, frequency, and duration, the middle three boxes represent a continuum from symptoms (on the left) to strengths (on the right.) Mark whichever one of the three boxes best represents where you see your organization on this continuum. Use the area below each symptom/strength to make note of any observations or supporting evidence that led to your rating. *Note: This checklist is meant for planning purposes and not intended to be scored. Therefore, there is no numerical value assigned to the three boxes.*

Conducting an organizational assessment includes gathering many perspectives. It is important to recognize that the perspective of the frontline workforce might be different from that of leadership. It is also helpful to know how clients and community partners perceive the organization.

Change teams can use this information to develop goals by identifying symptoms and prioritizing the ones that have the most negative impact on the organization. The goal is to turn symptoms into strengths. You can use the corresponding strength description as your objective and the noted observations to help identify measurable indicators of progress.

Cognitive symptoms and strengths

Scarcity thinking There is a constant pressure to find ways to cut expenses and make do with less.				**Abundant thinking** Leaders prioritize resources so that programs and staff have what they need to succeed.
Observations:				

Finger pointing When things go wrong, there is a constant scramble to assign blame elsewhere.				**Accountability** Both leaders and staff step up to take responsibility for problems and solutions.
Observations:				

Failure to learn from mistakes The organization keeps repeating the same mistakes. Employees are expected to blindly follow rigid procedures.				Innovation Questioning and experimentation within the scope of the organization's mission and values is encouraged. Both success and failures are embraced as learning opportunities.
Observations:				

Fixed perception Leadership perceives most employees as having fixed roles and capabilities. This is sometimes echoed in staffs' perception of service recipients.				Growth perception The organization recognizes that all people have the potential for growth and change. Leadership develops and inspires employees at all levels.
Observations:				

Denial Leaders are unaware of the struggles of their employees and the needs of the community.				Awareness Leaders and employees have an accurate perception of the challenges their organization might face.
Observations:				

Polarization There is a strong us-against-them mentality between management and front line, different departments, and even staff and clients.				Shared ownership All employees and members of the service community have a sense of shared ownership in outcomes of the work. Support for each other is freely given.
Observations:				

Emotional symptoms and strengths

Fear Fear is the primary motivator.				Sense of safety Employees and the service community feel safe in the knowledge that they will be treated fairly. This includes being safe to express opinions and perceptions that differ from leadership.
Observations:				

Numbing Negative emotions surface in the form of low morale, absenteeism, and high turnover. There is a failure to validate these human responses.				Attunement Leaders and employees are attuned to the emotional pulse of the organization and service community. There are healthy avenues for emotional expression.
Observations:				

Conflict Conflicts go unresolved, allowing anger to fester.				Conflict resolution Conflicts are viewed as learning opportunities and addressed in a timely manner.
Observations:				

Reactionary responses The organization reacts to situations based on past negative perceptions and emotions.				Responsible decision-making Decisions are guided by agency values, future expectations, and those most impacted by the decision.
Observations:				

Behavioral Symptoms and Strengths

Punitive practices There are attempts to control behavior through punitive methods.				**Empowerment** The organization encourages accountability through clear expectations, learning opportunities and choice.
Observations:				

Closed communication Needed information is not shared with everyone. Leaders only value and rely on the opinions of an elite few.				**Transparency** Information flow is bidirectional, clear, and open. Leadership seeks to learn from all members of the organization and service community. Regular feedback is encouraged.
Observations:				

Disconnect The actions of leaders and practitioners routinely contradict professed values.				**Integrity** Practices accurately reflect agency values.
Observations:				

Disorganization Tasks are performed inconsistently or do not always lead to desired results. People wonder about the purpose of what they are told to do.				**Purpose driven** There is a clear connection between the work being done and the mission of the organization.
Observations:				

Value Alignment

One of the unfortunate symptoms of a compassion-fatigues organization is that their professed values are no longer reflected in day-to-day behaviors. It is helpful to begin by acknowledging where and when this contradiction is occurring. It is also important to identify what should be done instead to better reflect the values of the organization.

Using the following worksheet, list the organization's values in the first column. In the second column, list examples of the behaviors within the organization that are a contradiction to each value. These behaviors will become the old way. In the third column, list the behaviors that you would like to do instead. This reflects the new way.

This activity is useful to do in leadership groups, departmental groups or focus groups representing members of the organization.

Value Alignment

VALUES	OLD WAY	NEW WAY

Value-Based Decision Making

The day in and day out decisions of helping professionals can be impaired by emotions. This is especially true when the emotion has triggered us into a survival mode, causing reactive decisions. A more effective decision-making device is to practice value-based decisions.

Values are the core principles and beliefs that we hold dear. Values have an emotional component but require greater deliberation. Because they are shaped and developed throughout our lifetime, values can offer more truth and stability than a fleeting emotion. In the navigation system analogy, values are more like the compass that reliably points north. It provides both consistent and accurate information on where we are and which direction we need to be headed.

To practice value-based decisions, use the following worksheet to answer these questions:

- **What is the prevailing emotion?** Begin by acknowledging the emotion without judgment. Remember that emotions themselves are not right or wrong; they are a necessary part of being human.

- **What outdated perceptions might be influencing my current emotional state?** Examining our perceptions can help us root out negative or inaccurate thoughts that keep us stuck in unhelpful response patterns.

- **What are my top three core values?** Prioritizing what is most important to us helps ensure we are acting in ways that guide us in the direction we want to go.

- **What are the guiding principles to which I need to adhere?** Both professionally and personally, it is helpful to have a standard set of precepts that remain the same, regardless of our current situation.

- **What is the response that best reflects these values and principles?** We are what we do. Decisions based on what you deeply value will always get you closer to your true goals than ones based on immediate relief or reward.

Value-Based Decision Making

EMOTIONS

PERCEPTIONS

VALUES

1. _____
2. _____
3. _____

PRINCIPLES

_____
_____
_____

Possible

Rank which is best
reflection of values
and principles 1-5

_____
_____
_____
_____
_____
_____

Best Response:

Conflict Resolution Process

Follow these eight steps using the following worksheet:

1. Begin by setting any ground rules that anyone needs to feel safe in this process. The facilitator can begin by offering suggestions, such as listening without interrupting while others are speaking, everyone has a right to their emotions and perceptions, etc.

2. Allow each person or group to identify the emotions involved for them in this conflict. Each person or group should have an opportunity to speak uninterrupted. Instruct each to listen while the other person is sharing how they feel. The emotions are recorded in the boxes labeled "Emotion." Each of the opposing viewpoints has its own box. (If the conflict is between two individuals, the facilitator can choose to have each reflect what they heard.)

3. Next, each person or group shares their perspective one at a time without interruption. Again, the other person is instructed to listen. Each side can clarify any misperceptions when it is their turn.

4. In the center box, record the points that everyone agreed on. The facilitator can offer suggestions to get them started.

5. Each person or group takes turns identifying what they need in relation to the conflict.

6. Each person or group takes turns offering what they are willing to do in response to the other's needs.

7. As a point of agreement is reached, it can be recorded in the center box.

8. Conclude the process with a quick emotion word check-in to describe how the participants felt about the process. Restate what each is willing to do and offer follow-up, as necessary.

Conflict Resolution Process

Emotions	Perceptions

What I need	What we can agree on	What I'm willing to do
. . . .		. . . .
What I'm willing to do		What I need

Emotions	Perceptions

Group Processing

A simple practice that can be implemented by organizations is routine processing. Routine processing is a method of acknowledging experiences that offers emotional and concrete support.

Unprocessed events tend to cause rumination that can lead to disconnection. Putting words to what is experienced allows helping professionals to move away from a reactionary state, calming our stress response.

Processing should not be confused with incident inquiries, in which the purpose is to get an accurate account of a critical incident to identify the cause. Routine processing is a practice in which judging and blaming need to be suspended.

Processing can be done in a formal group setting when there has been a shared traumatic experience or done more informally and routinely.

Organizations can implement more formal procedures for processing. They can be incorporated into existing meetings and daily routines.

The following worksheet can be used to help process events or situations that have had a triggering effect on the organization.

Group Processing

Situation summary (keep it brief, one person describes events and then allows clarifying questions)

Thought reactions

What was your first thought or thoughts after learning of or witnessing the situation/incident?

What was the most challenging aspect from your perspective?

Feelings

What have been some of the strongest emotions you have been experiencing?

What body sensations did you experience?

What are some losses you or the team have experienced?

Response

What was my response?

Reflection

What worked well?

Is there anything we could do differently in the future?

What is your self-care plan?

How can you support each other moving forward?

About The Author

Michelle Graff is the founder of Cultivating Human Resiliency and the author of *The Compassion Fatigued Organization*. After more than twenty years in social services, she now focuses on helping the helping professional.

As a resiliency cultivator, she provides training and consultation to both public and private human service agencies. Over the past twenty-two years, Michelle has developed and presented hundreds of trainings on everything from trauma and the brain to interpersonal and leadership skills. Her experience working with human service professionals and organizations has provided an insider's perspective on the impact of secondary trauma. Compassion fatigue has become her most requested topic.

Michelle lives and works in Kansas City, where she enjoys learning, creating, and spending time with family and friends.

For more information on Compassion Fatigue:

The Compassion Fatigued Organization:

Restoring Compassion to Helping Professionals

Michelle Graff

Cultivating Human Resiliency

resiliencyonline.com

Made in the USA
Monee, IL
21 May 2024

58738354R10042